Bible Verses for Today

Daily Scripture Reading Plan, Bible Study
& Creative Journal for 365 Days for Women

Created by Valeria Wolfl

ISBN: 978-1-7779753-0-2

Thank you for your purchase!

I am thrilled you chose to purchase this book. I worked very hard to create a functional and creative bible study journal for my sisters in Christ. I would like to hear your opinion and thoughts about the book.

Can you please post a review on amazon? It will only take a few minutes, but it will make a huge difference to me.

Thank you!

God bless you.

Valeria

Contact: biblestudyprintables@gmail.com

Topic index

Topic index

Topic index

Topic index

Topic index

BLESSED

Trust in
the *LORD*
with all your heart.
Proverbs 3:5

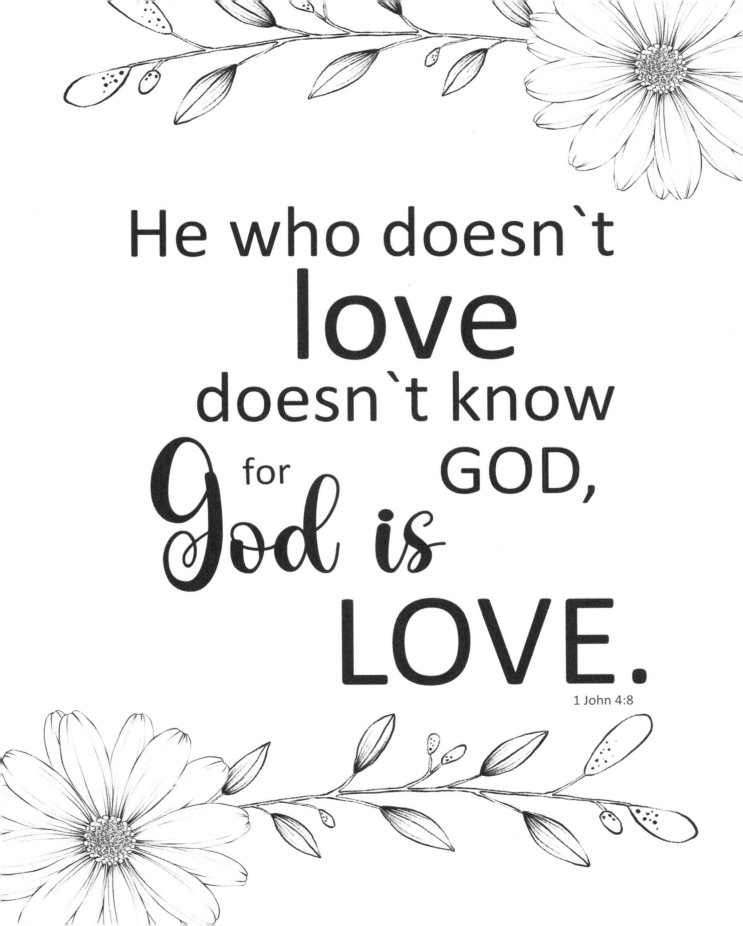

He who doesn`t **love** doesn`t know for *God is* GOD, **LOVE.**

1 John 4:8

Scripture

1. What do you see?
2. What didn't you notice before?
3. Is there repetition, comparison or contrast?
4. What do you feel like God is telling you in this verse?
5. What lesson or message is being portrayed?
6. What jumps out to you in the passage?
7. Who is it written to?
8. What's one thing you didn't notice before?
9. What seems interesting or unusual?
10. What comes before and after the text?
11. What does it say about God?
12. What does it say about people?
13. What does it say about the relationship between God and people?
14. What do I learn about relating to God?
15. What do I learn about relating to others?
16. What does this say about the human condition?

Prayer

Pray that the seed (the Scripture you have just studied) falls on good soil in your heart, so that it will take root and produce fruit.
Praise God for His attributes revealed in the passage.
Confess any sin that has come to light during this time of studying.
Thank Him for His Word and His care.
Ask the Holy Spirit to continue growing you into a disciple of Jesus.

1. Is there anything I need to confess?
2. Is there any sin from which I need to repent?
3. What can I be thankful for because of this passage?
4. How can I praise God because of this passage?

Application

1. How does it apply to me?
2. Is there a specific action i need to take or a confession i need to make?
3. How can I apply what I have just read to my walk with the Lord?
4. Do I need to make changes?
5. Do I need to take an action?
6. Is there:
   a) a command to obey?
   b) a promise to claim?
   c) a sin to avoid?
   d) an application to make?
7. What response does God want from me?
8. What does it look like for me to believe and obey this Scripture in a genuine, non-superficial way?
9. Do I need help in believing or heeding this Scripture?
10. How can I praise God because of this passage?
11. How can I encourage myself with this passage today?
12. How might I encourage others with this passage today?
13. How does this passage deepen my longing for the return of Christ and the joys of heaven?
14. What does God want me to understand/think?
15. What does God want me to believe?
16. What does God want me to desire?
17. What does God want me to do?

We walk by FAITH, not by SIGHT.

2 Corinthians 5:7

Day 1 – Faith

Romans 10:17 - Hebrews 12:2 - 2 Corinthians 5:7

Day 2 – Troubles

Nahum 1:7 - Psalm 138:7 - Psalm 121:1-2

Day 3 - Patience

Isaiah 40:31 - Psalm 37:7 - Psalm 40:1

Day 4 - Strengths

Daniel 10:19 - Ephesians 3:16-17 - Isaiah 40:31

Day 5 – Sufficiency

Philippians 4:19 - 2 Corinthians 3:5 - 2 Corinthians 12:9

Day 6 – Companion

Hebrews 13:5 - John 15:12-14 - 1 Corinthians 1:9

Day 7 – Guide for life

Psalm 119:105 - John 8:31-32 - Psalm 32:8

Day 8 – Feeling Discouraged

Hebrews 10:35-35 - Psalm 138:7 - Psalm 27:14

Day 9 – Obedience

John 14:15 - Acts 5:29 - Psalm 143:10

Day 10 – Priorities

Proverbs 22:4 - Hebrews 6:1-11

Day 11 – Speaking the word of God

Mark 11:23 - Luke 17:6 - Deuteronomy 18:18

Day 12 – Feeling Dissatisfied

Philippians 4:12-13 - Psalm 63:1-5 - Proverbs 12:4

Day 13 – Righteousness

2 Corinthians 5:21 - Philippians 3:9 - Romans 3:24-26

Day 14 – Overwhelmed

Psalm 69:16-18 - Psalm 116:1-2 - John 14:27

Day 15 - God's love

Romans 8:37-39 - 1 John 4:10-12 - Jeremiah 31:3

Day 16 - Conflict

Romans 12:17-18 - Matthew 5:9 - 2 Corinthians 13:11

Day 17 – Suffering

Psalm 91:1-2 - John 14:27 - Philippians 3:10-11

Day 18 – Praying for others

James 5:16 - Romans 15:30 - Luke 6:27-28

Day 19 – Serving The Lord

Joshua 24:14-15 - 2 Peter 1:3-4 - Luke 10:38-42

Day 20 – Repentance

Acts 2:38 - Luke 15:7 - Luke 3:8

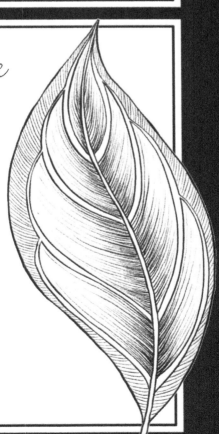

Day 21 – Our Lord

Philippians 2:9-11 - Acts 2:36 - Romans 14:8 - Acts 2:25

Day 22 – Our divine brother

Hebrews 2:1 - Galatians 4:6-7 - Matthew 12:50

Day 23 - Will of God

Psalm 32:8 - Proverbs 16:3 - James 1:5

Day 24 - Self-worth

1 Corinthians 4:1-4 - Colossians 3:10-11 - Psalm 139:13–14

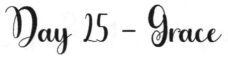

Day 25 – Grace

Ephesians 4:7 - Acts 20:24 - 2 Corinthians 12:9

Day 26 – Guilt

2 Corinthian 5:17 - Romans 8:1 - Isaiah 43:25

Day 27 – Worshiping God

John 4:23-24 - Deuteronomy 6:13-14 - Isaiah 25:1

Day 28 – Hope

Romans 8:31-33 - 2 Corinthians 4:18 - Romans 12:12

Day 29 – Living like Jesus

Matthew 5:14-16 - Romans 14:8 - 1 Peter 4:11

Day 30 – God's faithfulness

1 Corinthians 1:8-9 - 2 Timothy 2:13 - 2 Thessalonians 3:3

Day 31 – Who I am in Christ (1)

Ephesians 1:4 - Romans 1:6 - Ephesians 1:7

Day 32 – Who I am in Christ (2)

Philippians 3:8-9 - Romans 5:10 - Matthew 20:28

Day 33 – Who I am in Christ (3)

John 8:36 - Romans 3:28 - Romans 15:7

Day 34 – Money

Matthew 6:24 - Hebrews 13:5 - 1 Timothy 6:9-10

Day 35 - Honor God with money

Romans 13:7 - Deuteronomy 15-7 - Proverbs 3:9-10

Day 36 - Prayers

1 Peter 3:12 - Matthew 21:22 - Philippians 4:6-7

Day 37 – What The Holy Spirit does (1)

John 14:16 - John 16:8-9 - John 16-14

Day 38 – What The Holy Spirit does (2)

John 14:26 - Ephesians 1:13 - John 16:3

Day 39 – What The Holy Spirit does (3)

Romans 8.26 - Acts 1:8 - John 14:26

Day 40 – The mustard seed

Matthew 13:31-31 - Mark 4:30-32 - Luke 13:18-19

Day 41 – The unmerciful servant

Matthew 18:23-35

Day 42 – Proverbs: Wisdom

Proverbs 8:22-31 - Proverbs 2:6-7 - Proverbs 1-7 - Proverbs 8:10-11

Day 43 – Understanding humanity

Proverbs 29:13 - Jeremiah 17:9-10 - Proverbs 28:26 - Proverbs 27:19

Day 44 – Description of a wise person (1)

Proverbs 13:5-6 - Proverbs 12:17 - Proverbs 16:6 - Proverbs 12:22

Day 45 – Description of a wise person (2)

Proverbs 28:13 - Proverbs 17:27 - Proverbs 20:22 - Proverbs 12:22

Day 46 – Description of a wise person (3)

Proverbs 27:2 - Proverbs 17:9 - Proverbs 12:16

Day 47 – Description of a wise person (4)

Proverbs 12:8 - Proverbs 14:16 - Proverbs 16:23

Day 48 – A wise person's relationships with others

Proverbs 22:24-25 - Proverbs 27:10
Proverbs 3:27-28 - Proverbs 25:17 - Proverbs 3:29

Day 49 – A wise person's possessions

Proverbs 11:4 - Proverbs 16:16 - Proverbs 3:9-10
Proverbs 22:16 - Proverbs 29:7 - Proverbs 12:10

Day 50 – The 6 things The LORD hates

Proverbs 6:16-19

Day 51 – The return of Jesus

1 Thessalonians 4:13-18 - 1 Corinthians 15:51-57 - Titus 2:13 - Matthew

Day 52 – Our example is Jesus

1 Peter 2:21 - 1 John 2:6 - Mark 10:43-45 - John 13:34

Day 53 – Our fulfillment is Jesus

Matthew 5:6 - Psalm 103:5 - John 6:35 - John 4:13-14

Day 54 – Praise

1 peter 2:9 - Hebrews 13:15 - Psalm 48:1 - Psalm 34:1

Day 55 – The talents

Matthew 25:14-30 - 1 Peter 4:10-11

Day 56 – Assurance of salvation

1 John 5:11-13 - Romans 10:9 - John 3:16-17

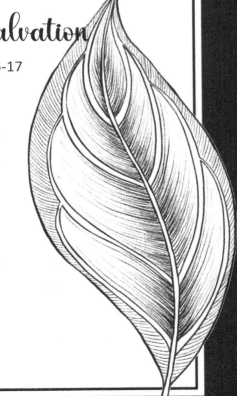

Day 57 – Peace and Joy

John 14:27 - Matthew 11:28 - 1 Peter 1:8-9 - John 16:24 - 2 Thessalonians 3:16

Day 58 – Comfort

Psalm 147:3 - Revelation 7:17 - Psalm 23:4 - Matthew 5:4

Day 59 – Security

Psalm 139:13-16 - Isaiah 40:31 - 2 Timothy 1:7

Day 60 – Fear

Psalm 118:6-7 - Psalm 23:4 - Deuteronomy 31:8 - John 14: 27

Day 61 – Confusion

1 John 4:1-2 - Isaiah 41:10 - Psalm 111:10 - Romans 12:2

Day 62 – Guidance

John 16:3 - Isaiah 42:16 - Psalm 139-9-12 - Proverbs 16:9

Day 63 – God's goodness and mercy

Psalm 69:13-17 - Micah 7:18 - 2 Peter 1:4 - Romans 8:28

Day 64 – Temptation

1 Corinthians 10:12-13 - Hebrews 2:18
Ephesians 6:10-12 - James 1:12

Day 65 – Overcoming temptations

Matthew 26:41 - Galatians 5:16-17 - James 4:7
Romans 12:21 - Ephesians 6:10-17

Day 66 – God's presence

Isaiah 42:2 - Psalm 145:18-19 - 2 Corinthians 4:8-9 - Matthew 18:20

Day 67 – Anger

Ephesians 4:26-27 - James 1:19-20 - Romans 12:17-19 - Proverbs 17:27-28

Day 68 – Understanding

James 1:5 - Proverbs 3:5-6 - Isaiah 55:8-9 - Jeremiah 33:2-3

Day 69 - Tired

Isaiah 12:2 - Isaiah 40:28-31 - Philippians 4:13 - 2 Corinthians 12:9 - Matthew 11:28:30

Day 70 - The rich fool

Luke 12:16-21 - Hebrew 13:5

Day 11 – Lonely

Psalm 107:9 - Romans 8:39 - Matthew 28:20 - John 16:32

Day 12 – Impatient

Colossians 3:12 - Ephesians 4:2 - Psalm 24:17 - Proverbs 16:32

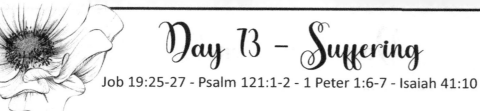

Day 13 – Suffering

Job 19:25-27 - Psalm 121:1-2 - 1 Peter 1:6-7 - Isaiah 41:10

Day 14 – Afraid

Joshua 1:5 - Psalm 20:7 - Psalm 27:1 - Psalm 56:11 - Matthew 10:28 - Romans 8:31

Day 75 – Depressed

Numbers 6:24-26 - Isaiah 61:1 - John 16:33

Day 76 – Doubting salvation

Psalm 103:12 - John 5:24 - John 6:47 - Philippians 1:6

Day 77 – Commitment to God

Luke 9:29 - Mark 8:35 - Joshua 24:15 - Matthew 6:33

Day 78 – False teachers

Matthew 7:15 - Galatians 1:8 - Deuteronomy 18:20 - Matthew 24:24
1 John 4:1-6 - Matthew 7:15-20

Day 79 – Humility

Matthew 5:3 - Romans 12:3 - Micah 6:8
Proverbs 22:4 - 1 Peter 5:6

Day 80 – The faithful servant

Matthew 24:45-51 - Luke 16:10 - 1 Corinthians 4:2

Day 81 – Time to pray

Romans 1:9-10 - Ephesians 6:18 - Colossians 1:3
1 Thessalonians 1:2, 2:13, 5:17 - 2 Timothy 1:3

Day 82 – Great escapes (1)

Genesis 31:1-55

Day 83 – What God has done about sin

Romans 6:2-16

Day 84 – What we have as God's children

Romans 5:8,10,11,17-21

Day 85 – A profile of a strong church

Romans 15:1-8

Day 86 – Pleasing God (1)

John 8:29 - 2 Corinthians 5:9 - Galatians 6:8 - Colossians 1:9-10

Day 87 – Pleasing God (2)

1 Thessalonians 2:4 - 1 Thessalonians 4:1 - Hebrews 11:6 - 1 John 3:22

Day 88 – Set an example

Matthew 11:29 - Philippians 3:17 - 1 Timothy 1:16 - 1 Peter 5:3

Day 39 – Do not give up – Purpose – Plan – Prize

1 Corinthians 9:24-27 - Galatians 7-10
Ephesians 6:10-20 - Philippians 3:12-1
2 Timothy 2:1-13

Day 90 – The place of honor

Luke 14:7-11 - Proverbs 29:23 - Matthew 23:12

Day 91 – Justice

Leviticus 19:15 - Psalm 82:3-4 - Isaiah 30:18 - Micah 6:8 - Malachi 3:5

Day 92 – Gossiping

Psalm 34:12-13 - Proverbs 11:13 - Proverbs 17:9
Ephesians 4:29

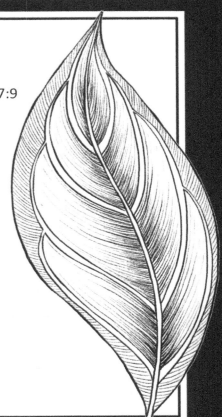

Day 93 – Friendship

Proverbs 17:17 - Proverbs 27:17 - Ecclesiastes 4:12

Day 94 – Giving

Proverbs 11:24-25 - Malachi 3:10 - 2 Corinthians 9:7

Day 95 – Great escapes (2)

Exodus 2:11-15 - Exodus 12:28-42

Day 96 – Faith

Matthew 17:20 - Romans 10:17 - Hebrews 11:1 - Hebrews 11:6

Day 97 – Government

Luke 20:25 - Acts 5:28-29 - Titus 3:1

Day 98 – The wise and foolish builders

Matthew 7:24-27 - Luke 6:47-49

Day 99 – Good works

Matthew 25:40 - Romans 12:20-21 - Galatians 6:7-11

Day 100 – Obedience

1 Samuel 2:30 - 1 Samuel 15:22 - John 14:23

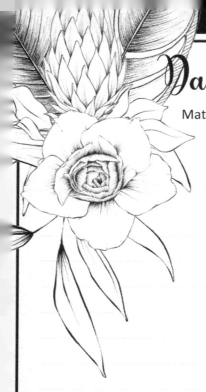

Day 101 – Forgiving others

Matthew 18:21-22 - Mark 11:25 - Colossians 33:13
Philippians 3:13-14

Day 102 – Christian fellowship

Ephesians 5:2,19,30 - Colossians 2:2 - Luke 24:13-15 - Psalm 55:14

Day 103 - God's faithfulness

1 Thessalonians 5:24 - Genesis 9:16 - Joshua 23:14 - Psalm 36:5

Day 104 - Longing for heaven

Psalm 73:25-26 - John 14:2-3 - 1 Corinthians 2:9

Day 105 – Prayer

Matthew 6:6 - John 14:13-14 - 1 Timothy 2:1,8

Day 106 – Loving God

John 14:15,21 - Mark 12:29-30 - 1 John 4:19-21

Day 107 – The good Samaritan

Luke 10:30-37

Day 108 – Great escapes (3)

Joshua 2:1-24

Day 109 – Marks of a false Gospel

Galatians 2:21 - 3:12 - 4:10 - 5:4 - 3:26-28

Day 110 – Marks of a true gospel

Galatians 1:11-12 - 2:20 - 3:14 - 3:21-22 - 5:24-25

Day 111 – Who I am in Christ (4)

Romans 3:24 - Romans 8:1-2 - 1 Corinthians 1:2,30 - 15:22

Day 112 – Sinful human desires

Romans 8:5-7 - Galatians 5:16,24 - Colossians 3:5

Day 113 – The old self is dead

Galatians 2:20 - Romans 6:6 - Ephesians 4:22-24
Romans 6:22

Day 114 – The fruit of the Spirit

Galatians 5:22-26

Day 115 – Do it for others

Romans 12:10 - Ephesians 5:19 - Mark 9:50 - John 13:14 - Romans 15:7,14
Colossians 3:13 - Romans 14:3 - James 15:16

Day 116 – Blameless

Hebrews 9:14 - Peter 1:19 - Ephesians 5:27 - Colossians 1:22
2 Peter 3:14 - Jude 1:24

Day 117 – Great escapes (4)

Judges 3:15-30

Day 118 – The Mustard seed

Luke 13:18-19

Day 119 – Who I am in Christ (5)

2 Corinthians 5:17,21 - Ephesians 1:3-13

Day 120 – Repentance

Psalm 32:5 - Acts 2:38 - Luke 15:7

Day 121 – God's riches given to us (1)

Romans 2:4 - 9:23 - 11:33 - 2 Corinthians 8:9 - Ephesians 1:7,18 - 2:4,7

Day 122 – God's riches given to us (2)

Ephesians 3:8.16 - Philippians 4:19 - Colossians 1:27 - 2:2

Day 123 – The seal of the Spirit (1)

Romans 8:9 - 1 Corinthians 6:17 - Romans 8:14-17 - Galatians 4:6-7 - 1 Corinthians 12:13

Day 124 – The seal of the Spirit (2)

1 Corinthians 6:19 - Galatians 5:22-23 - 2 Corinthians 3:18 - Ephesians 3:16-20

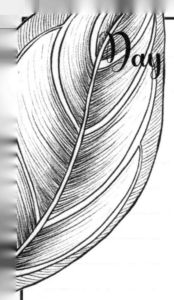

Day 125 – The seal of the Spirit (3)

Ephesians 2:22 - 1 Corinthians 12:4-11

Day 126 – The lost coin

Luke 15:8-10

Day 127 – Great escapes (5)

Judges 1:3 - 1 Kings 19:1-18

Day 128 – Who I am in Christ (6)

Ephesians 2:6,10,13 - 3:6,12,29-30

Day 129 – Prayers for opportunities to minister

Romans 1:10 - Philippians 1:19 - Colossians 4:3 - 1 Thessalonians 3:10

Day 130 – God's love

Psalm 63:1,3 - Psalm 85:6 - 1 John 4:18-19

Day 131 – Answered prayers

Isaiah 65:24 - Matthew 7:7-8 - 21:22 - 18:19-20 - John 14:13

Day 132 – Jesus is our example

Ephesians 5:1-2 - John 13:14 -15,34 - 1 John 3:16

Day 133 – Prayers for knowledge and insight

Ephesians 1:18-19 - Philippians 1:9 - Colossians 1:9

Day 134 – Who I am in Christ (7)

Colossians 2:10-11 - 2 Timothy 2:10

Day 135 – Great escapes (6)

Acts 9:23-25 - 12:1-11

Day 136 – Prayers for progress and growth

2 Corinthians 13:9 - 1 Thessalonians 3:13

Day 137 – Growing spiritually (1)

2 Peter 3:18 - 2 Timothy 2:15 - 1 Timothy 4:5 - Hebrews 6:1

Day 138 – Growing spiritually (2)

2 Peter 1:5-8 - Ephesians 3:14-19 - Psalms 92:12 - Philippians 1:6,9-10

Day 139 – Three stages of perfection

Perfect Relationship: Colossians 2:8-10 - Perfect Progress: Philippians 3:1-15
Completely Perfect - Philippians 3:20-21, 1:6

Day 140 – Three Tenses of salvation

Justification (past) - saved from the penalty of sin: Romans 6:23 - John 3:16-18 - Ephesians 2:8,9
Sanctification (present)- saved from the power of sin: Galatians 5:16,25 - 1 Thessalonians 4:3
Philippians 1:6 - 1 Peter 1:15 - Romans 8:23
Glorification (future) - saved from the presence of sin:
Colossians 3:4 - 1 John 3:2 - 1 Corinthians 15:51-53

Day 141 - Prayers for living a holy life

2 Corinthians 3:17 - Colossians 1:10 - 2 Thessalonians 1:11

Day 142 - How to live a holy life (1)

To be holy means to be set apart or separate from sin and evil.
1 Peter 1:16 - 1 Thessalonians 4:3-8
Knowing and obeying God's Word is key - John 17:17

Day 143 – How to live a holy life (2)

Romans 12:1-2 - Matthew 5:16 - Romans 6:6 - Galatians 5:16 - 1 john 1:9

Day 144 – Great escapes (1)

Acts 16:22-40

Day 145 – The Prodigal son

Luke 15:11:32

Day 146 – Pleasing God

Isaiah 43:7,21 - John 4:23-24 - 1 Peter 2:5-9 - Hebrews 13:15-16

Day 147 – Salvation

Romans 3:23 - 6:23 - 5:8 - John 3:36 - Ephesians 2:8-9

Day 148 – When in doubt about God

Romans 10:17 - 1 Peter 4:12-13 - Mark 11:22-24

Day 149 – Peace

Isaias 26:3 - John 14:27 - Philippians 4:7-7 - Romans 5:1

Day 150 – Prayer for encouragement

Ephesians 1:16 - 3:16,19 - Colossians 1:3 - 1 Thessalonians 1:2

Day 151 – Training for the christian life

2 Timothy 2:5 - 4:7-8 - 1 Corinthians 9:24-27 - Philippians 3:13-14
1 Timothy 4:7-10

Day 152 – Called to suffer

Matthew 5:10-12 - 20:23 - Acts 5:41 - Romans 8:17
2 Corinthians 1:3-7 - Ephesians 3:13

Day 153 – Paul's Prayers – He prayed

Romans 10:1 - 2 Corinthians 13:7,9 - Ephesians 1:17 - 3:16-19
Philippians 1:4,9 - Colossians 1:9 - 1 Thessalonians 3:10 - Philemon 1:6

Day 154 – Paul's Prayers – He asked

Romans 15:30-31 - Ephesians 6:19-20 - Colossians 4:3 - 1 Thessalonians 5:25
2 Thessalonians 3:1-2

Day 155 – How to encourage

1 Thessalonians 5:11-23

Day 156 – The ten minas

Luke 19:11:27

Day 157 – Money and contentment

Proverbs 11:4 - Jeremiah 17:11 - Ecclesiastes 5:10-11
James 2:1-9 - 1 Timothy 6:17-19 - Proverbs 19:1 - Hebrews 13:5

Day 158 – Be strong

Romans 4:20 - 2 Corinthians 12:9 - Ephesians 6:10-11
Philippians 4:13 - 1 Timothy 1:12

Day 159 – Heavenly rewards (1)

Mathew 16:24-27 - 19:28-30 - Romans 6:8 - 8:17

Day 160 – Heavenly rewards (2)

1 Corinthians 15:42-58 - Colossians 3:3-4
1 Thessalonians 4:13-18 - Revelation 3:21 - 21:1-27

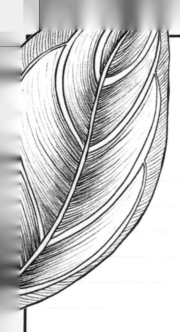

Day 161 – Patience

Romans 5:3 - Hebrews 12:1-2 - James 1:2-4
Romans 15:4-5 - James 1:3-4

Day 162 – God's mercy

Luke 1:50 - Ephesians 2:4-5 - Hebrews 4:16 - Luke 6:36 - Deuteronomy 4:31

Day 163 – God's blessings

Ephesians 1:3-4 - Romans 10:12-13 - James 1:17 - Numbers 6:24-26

Day 164 – The cost of being a disciple

Luke 14:25-35

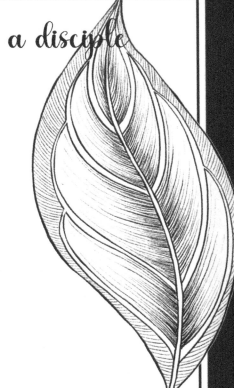

Day 165 – What Jesus did to our sins

Hebrews 2:17 - 8:12 - 10:17 - 9:15,26 - 1:12,18,19

Day 166 – The word of God

Isaiah 55:11 - Jeremiah 23:29 - John 6:63 - Ephesians 6:17 - Hebrews 4:12
1 Peter 1:23 - Revelation 1:15 - 2:12

Day 167 – Obedience or sacrifices

1 Samuel 15:22-23 - Psalm 40:6-9 - Hosea 6:6 - Micah 6:6-8 - Matthew 9:13

Day 168 – What God has for us

Hebrews 20:10,14 - 21:2-5,10-14 - 22:1-3,5

Day 169 – Finance

1 Corinthians 16:2 - Luke 6:38 - 2 Corinthians 9:6-8
Matthew 19:29 - Philippians 4:29

Day 170 – God's way

Isaiah 55:8-9 - Jeremiah 33:3 - Hosea 6:3 - Psalm 18:30

Day 111 – The Almighty

1 Chronicles 29:11 - Jeremiah 32:27 - Revelation 1:8
Psalm 145:3 - 1 Chronicles 29:12

Day 112 – Acknowledging God

John 4:15 - Romans 14:11 - Romans 10:9
Psalm 32:5 - 1 John 2:23

Day 173 – Beauty

1 Peter 3:3-4 - 1 Samuel 16:7 - Psalm 139:13-14
2 Corinthians 4:16

Day 174 – The wedding banquet

Matthew 22:2-14

Day 175 – Blameless

Psalm 15:2-3 - Psalm 119:1 - Proverbs 2:7
Philippians 2:14-16 - Hebrews 5:9

Day 176 – Calling

John 15:16 - 1 Thessalonians 5:24 - 2 Thessalonians 2:14
2 Timothy 1:9 - 1 Peter 1:15-16

Day 177 – Comforter

2 Corinthians 1:3-4 - Psalm 94:19 - Revelation 7:16-17 - 2 Corinthians 1:5 - John 14:16

Day 178 – Heaven

1 Thessalonians 4:16-17 - Colossians 3:2 - John 14:2 - Matthew 6:19-20 - Jeremiah 23:24

Day 179 – Gratitude

1 Thessalonians 5:16-18 - Philippians 4:6-7 - 1 Chronicles 16:34 - Colossians 3:15
1 Corinthians 15:57

Day 180 – Temptation

1 Corinthians 10:13 - James 1:12 - Matthew 26:41 - James 1:13
James 1:3 - Hebrews 4:15

Day 181 – Harvest

2 Corinthians 9:10 - Galatians 6:9 - Proverbs 3:9
Matthew 6:26 - James 3:18

Day 182 – The net

Matthew 13:47-50

Halfway through the year

Jeremiah 17:7-8

Day 183 – Praise

Isaiah 25:1 - Psalm 150:6 - Psalm 103:1 - Revelation 5:13 - Colossians 3:16

Day 184 – Rest

Matthew 11:28 - Matthew 11:29-30
Psalm 62:1 - Psalm 23:1-2

Day 185 – Weakness

2 Corinthians 12:10 - 2 Corinthians 12:9 - Psalm 73:26 - Romans 8:26 - Matthew 26:41

Day 186 – Repentance

2 Chronicles 7:14 - Acts 3:19 - Proverbs 28:13 - Matthew 3:8
2 Peter 3:9 - Matthew 4:17

Day 187 – Following

Deuteronomy 5:33 - Deuteronomy 31:8 - John 8:12 - Mark 8:34
Galatians 5:25 - 1 Peter 2:21

Day 188 – Learning

Psalm 32:8 - Proverbs 3:11-12 - Proverbs 12:1
1 John 2:27 - Titus 2:1

Day 189 – Reward

Colossians 3:23-24 - 1 Corinthians 15:58 - Matthew 25:21 - James 1:12 - Hebrews 11:6

Day 190 – Materialism

1 Timothy 6:7-8 - Ecclesiastes 5:10 - Matthew 6:19-20 - Hebrews 13:5 - Matthew 6:21

Day 191 – Angels

Matthew 26:53 - Hebrews 13:1-2 - Luke 15:10
Matthew 28:5-6 - Romans 8:38-39

Day 192 – Clothing

1 Peter 3:3-4 - Colossians 3:12 - Isaiah 61:10
Matthew 7:15 - Galatians 3:26-27

Day 193 – Crucifixion

1 Peter 2:24 - 1 Corinthians 1:18 - Galatians 2:20 - Philippians 2:6-8 - Luke 24:6-7

Day 194 - Devil

1 Peter 5:8 - Ephesians 6:11 - 2 Thessalonians 3:3 - James 4:7
1 John 3:8 - 1 Corinthians 10:13

Day 195 - New wine in old wineskins

Luke 5:37-38

Day 196 – Debt

Psalm 37:21 - Romans 13:8 - Romans 13:7
Luke 14:28 - Luke 6:30

Day 197 – Eternal life

John 10:28-30 - 1 Peter 5:10 - Romans 6:23 - Hebrews 7:25 - John 3:36

Day 198 – Equipment

Ephesians 6:11 - 2 Timothy 3:16-17 - Romans 8:26

Day 199 – The word of God

Hebrews 4:12 - Psalm 119:105 - Luke 11:28
Matthew 7:24 - Matthew 24:35

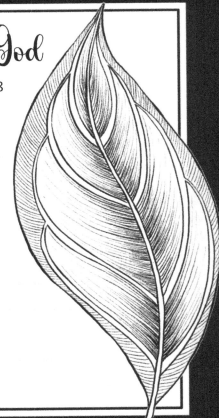

Day 200 – Valuable

Matthew 6:26 - Matthew 10:29-31
Isaiah 43:4 - Matthew 12:12

Day 201 – Trust

Proverbs 3:5-6 - Jeremiah 17:7-8 - Psalm 91:1-2 - 2 Corinthians 5:7 - James 1:6

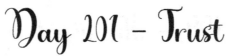

Day 202 – Thoughts

Psalm 139:23-24 - Mark 7:20-23 - Romans 12:2 - 1 Corinthians 2:11 - 1 Peter 1:13

Day 203 – Planning

Proverbs 16:3 - Luke 14:28 - Proverbs 16:9 - Isaiah 28:29 - Psalm 143:8

Day 204 – Recognizing God's Voice

1 Samuel 3:9 - John 10:4 - John 8:47 - John 14:26 - Romans 8:16

Day 205 – Old nature and your new one

Galatians 5:16-17 - Romans 6:12 - 1 Corinthians 9:27

Day 206 – The pearl

Matthew 13:45-46

Day 207 – Poverty

Philippians 4:12 - Proverbs 31:9 - 2 Corinthians 6:10
Psalm 34:6 - Proverbs 19:22 - Luke 3:11

Day 208 – Honesty

Proverbs 11:3 - Proverbs 12:22 - Acts 5:3-4

Day 209 – Humility

Proverbs 22:4 - Proverbs 15:33 - James 4:10 - Ephesians 4:2 - Philippians 2:3

Day 210 – Joy

1 Thessalonians 5:16-18 - Romans 12:12 - Isaiah 61:10
2 Corinthians 12:10 - Galatians 5:22-23

Day 211 – Kingdom

Matthew 6:33 - Luke 12:32 - John 3:3 - Ephesians 2:19-20 - Zechariah 14:9

Day 212 – Reconciliation

Ephesians 4:32 - 2 Corinthians 5:19 - Hebrews 12:14 - Colossians 3:13

Day 213 – Reliability

Deuteronomy 7:9 - Psalm 55:22 - Lamentations 3:22-23 - John 16:24

Day 214 - Transformation

2 Corinthians 3:18 - Romans 12:2 - Colossians 3:5 - Colossians 3:9-10

Day 215 - The tenants

Matthew 21:33-45

Day 216 – Abundant life

John 10:10 - Matthew 6:33 - Psalms 1:1-3
1 Corinthians 2:9 - Philippians 4:19

Day 217 – Accepting others

Romans 15:5-7 - Romans 15:7 - John 6:37 - 1 John 3:15

Day 218 – Ashamed

2 Timothy 2:15 - Mark 8:38 - Romans 1:16

Day 219 – Anointed

Luke 4:18 - Acts 2:38 - 1 John 2:20

Day 220 – Awesome God

Numbers 23:19 - Deuteronomy 10:17 - Psalms 92:15
Deuteronomy 32:4 - John 14:26

Day 221 – Confidence in God

Proverbs 3:26 - Philippians 1:6 - Hebrews 4:16 - 1 John 5:14 - Proverbs 3:5

Day 222 – Depression

Deuteronomy 31:8 - Psalms 34:17 - 1 Peter 5:6-7
Jeremiah 29:11

Day 223 – For a bad day

John 16:33 - 2 Thessalonians 3:16 - Jeremiah 29:11-12
Psalm 50:15 - Matthew 11:28-30

Day 224 – The pharisee and the tax collector

Luke 18:9-14

Day 225 – God's presence

Matthew 18:20 - 1 John 4:16 - Psalm 16:11 - Revelation 21:3 - Psalm 23:4

Day 226 – God's will

Romans 12:2 - 1 Thessalonians 5:16-19 - Ephesians 6:5-7 - 2 Corinthians 8:1-6

Day 227 – Jealousy

Proverbs 6:34 - James 3:16 - Deuteronomy 4:24
Psalm 79:5 - Exodus 20:17 - 1 Corinthians 3:3-5
Galatians 5:19-21

Day 228 – Missions

Isaiah 6:8 - Psalm 96:3 - Matthew 28:19, 20 - Acts 1:8

Day 229 – Regret

Philippians 3:13 - Psalm 34:4-5 - 2 Corinthians 7:10
Psalm 51:8-9 - Luke 22:61-62 - Genesis 6:6

Day 230 – Struggle

2 Corinthians 12:9-10 - Joshua 1:9 - Isaiah 54:17 - Psalms 34:17-18

Day 231 – Thanksgiving

Psalm 28:7 - 1 Chronicles 16:8 - Psalm 107:29-32 - 1 Thessalonians 5:18

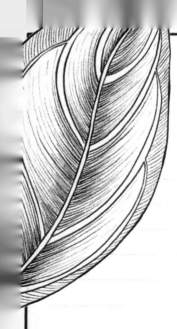

Day 232 – God's timing

Galatians 4:4-5 - Romans 5:6 - Ecclesiastes 3:11
Romans 11:25

Day 233 – Fear of the Lord and wisdom

Job 28:28 - Proverbs 1:7,9:10,15:33 - 1 Corinthians 1:19 - James 3:17

Day 234 – Respect

Romans 13:2 - 1 Thessalonians 5:12-13 - Hebrews 13:17 - 1 Peter 2:17 - Ephesians 6:2

Day 235 – Rapture

1 Thessalonians 4:16-17 - Daniel 12:1-3
1 Corinthians 15:52

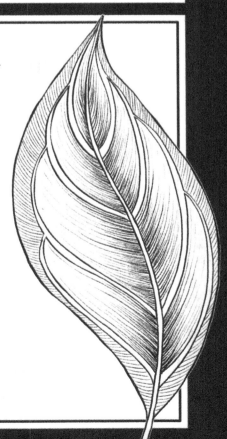

Day 136 – Freedom

Galatians 5:1 - 2 Corinthians 3:17 - Galatians 5:13
John 8:36 - 1 Peter 2:16

Day 137 – The unmerciful servant

Matthew 18:23-35

Day 238 – Spiritual maturity

Hebrews 6:1-4 - Hebrews 5:12-14 - Colossians 1:9-10

Day 239 – Attitude

Psalms 19:14 - Psalms 46:1-3 - Matthew 5:42-45 - Romans 12:1-2 - Philippians 4:4

Day 240 - Unity

1 Peter 3:8 - Acts 4:32 - Colossians 3:14
1 Corinthians 12:12 - 1 Corinthians 1:10

Day 241 - Father

Psalm 103:13 - 1 John 3:1 - Proverbs 3:11-12 - John 17:24

Day 242 - Messiah

Isaiah 9:6 - Acts 26:22-23 - Matthew 24:44

Day 243 - Lying

1 Peter 3:10-11 - Psalm 120:2 - Proverbs 12:22 - Psalm 34:13

Day 244 – Light

Psalm 119:105 - John 8:12 - John 1:5
Numbers 6:24-26

Day 245 – Materialism

1 Timothy 6:7-8 - Ecclesiastes 5:10 - Matthew 6:19-20 - Hebrews 13:5

Day 246 - Mind

Colossians 3:2 - Matthew 22:37 - Matthew 7:24 - James 3:13

Day 247 - The obedient servant

Luke 17:7-10

Day 248 - Idols

1 John 5:21 - Exodus 20:23 - Hosea 13:4 - Colossians 3:5

Day 249 - Law

Deuteronomy 6:6-7 - Romans 6:15 - 1 Corinthians 10:2 - Mark 12:31

Day 250 – Dependence

Proverbs 3:5-6 - Psalm 73:26 - Psalm 121:1-2 - John 15:5

Day 251 – Born again

2 Corinthians 5:17 - John 3:3 - 1 Peter 1:23 - Philippians 1:6 - John 3:5-6

Day 252 – Evangelism

Mark 16:15 - Acts 20:24 - Matthew 28:19-20
Romans 1:16 - 1 Peter 3:15

Day 253 – Receiving

Mark 11:24 - Colossians 3:23-24 - John 16:24 - Matthew 7:7 - Luke 6:38

Day 254 – The five heavenly crowns

1 Corinthians 9:24-25 - 1 Thessalonians 2:19 - 2 Timothy 4:8 - 1 Peter 5:4 - Revelation 2:10

Day 255 – Knowledge of God

Proverbs 2:6 - Romans 11:33 - Proverbs 1:7 - Proverbs 2:4-6 - 2 Corinthians 4:6

Day 256 – The spirit of prophecy

Revelation 19:10 - 2 Peter 1:21
Prophecy is communication from God to mankind.
What does the angel say who to worship? Why?

Day 257 – Work

Colossians 3:23-24 - Proverbs 16:3 - Colossians 3:17

Day 258 – The barren fig tree

Luke 13:6-9

Day 259 – Prophecy

1 Thessalonians 5:20-22 - 2 Peter 1:21 - Amos 3:7 - Matthew 7:15

Day 260 – Health

Exodus 23:25 - 3 John 1:2 - Proverbs 17:22
1 Corinthians 6:19-20 - Matthew 9:12

Day 261 – Confession

James 5:16 - Proverbs 28:13 - Psalm 32:5 - Romans 10:10

Day 262 – Acts of kindness

Luke 6:38 - Luke 6:27-31 - Acts 20:35 - John 15:23

Day 263 – Making a difference

Matthew 5:13-16 - Luke 12:33-34
Matthew 5:38-42

Day 264 - Relationship with God

John 3:16 - John 1:10-13 - Hebrews 11:6 - John 15:5

Day 265 - Victory in Christ

1 Corinthians 15:57 - Romans 8:31,39 - Philippians 4:13 - Ephesians 2:10

Day 266 – Hand of God

1 Peter 5:6 - John 10:29 - 1 Peter 3:21-22 - Romans 8:34

Day 267 – Keep from failing

Luke 1:37 - Philippians 4:13 - Micah 7-8 - 2 Timothy 1:7

Day 268 – Giving time to Jesus

Ephesians 5:16 - 1 john 3:16-18 - Jude 1:21

Day 269 – The yeast

Matthew 13:33 - Luke 13:20-21

Day 210 – Nearness

Psalm 34:17-18 - Philippians 4:5 - Ephesians 2:13 - 1 John 4:13

Day 211 – Compassion

Ephesians 4:32 - Lamentations 3:22-23
1 Peter 3:8 - 2 Corinthians 1:3-4

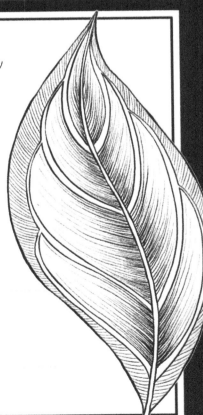

Day 272 – Comforter

Revelation 7:16-17 - 2 Corinthians 1:5
Psalm 118:5 - John 14:16

Day 273 – Kingdom

1 Corinthians 6:9-10 - Matthew 6:33 - 1 Chronicles 29:11 - Luke 12:32 - Matthew 4:17

Day 214 – Spirit

Ephesians 3:16-17 - Romans 15:13 - 2 Corinthians 3:17 - 1 Corinthians 6:19-20

Day 215 – Understanding God's way

Isaiah 55:8-9 - Jeremiah 33:3 - Psalm 18:30 - Psalm 138:8

Day 216 – The shrewd steward

Luke 16:1-13

Day 217 – Wait on God

Psalm 27:14 - Psalm 33:20 - Isaiah 40:31 - Hebrews 3:14

Day 218 - Faith

Mark 11:22-24 - 1 Peter 1:7-9 - Matthew 9:20-22

Day 219 - Eternity

1 John 5:11 - John 5:24 - 1 John 5:20 - John 6:51

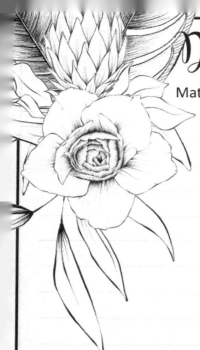

Day 280 – Serving God

Matthew 6:24 - Deuteronomy 13:4 - Romans 7:6

Day 281 – Savior

Romans 3:24-25 - Ephesians 2:4-5 - Romans 10:9

Day 282 - Lord

Philippians 29-11 - Romans 10:9-10 - Romans 12:1-2 - Isaiah 50:7

Day 283 - Love

1 John 4:7-12 - 1 John 4:16-19 - Proverbs 8:17

Day 284 – The lost sheep

Matthew 18:12-14

Day 285 – Peace

Isaiah 26:3 - Ephesians 2:13-14 - Romans 16:20 - Romans 5:1

Day 286 - Forgiveness

Ephesians 1:6-7 - Psalm 103:12 - Hebrews 8:12 - Colossians 3:13

Day 287 - Fellowship

1 John 1:3 - Revelation 3:20 - John 14:21,23

Day 288 – Example

1 Peter 2:21 - Mark 10:43-45 - Romans 15:5-7

Day 289 – Brother

Romans 8:29 - Galatians 3:26 - Romans 8:14 - Ephesians 2:19

Day 290 – Guardian

Psalm 3:3 - Psalm 61:3 - 1 Samuel 2:9

Day 291 – Security

1 Peter 1:3-5 - John 10:27-29 - 2 Thessalonians 3:3 - Jude 24-25

Day 292 – Feeling lonely

Hebrews 13:5 - Matthew 28:20 - Isaiah 41:10 - 1 Peter 5:7

Day 293 – Infallible authority

2 Timothy 3:16 - 2 Peter 1:20-21 - 1 Peter 1:23 - Proverbs 30:5

Day 294 – Stability

Matthew 24:35 - Ezekiel 12:25 - Isaiah 40:8 - Psalm 46:1

Day 295 – The sower

Matthew 13:3-9

Day 296 – Discouraged

1 Peter 6-9 - Psalm 138:7 - John 14:1
Philippians 1:6

Day 297 – Tempted

Hebrews 4:14-16 - 1 Corinthians 10:12-13 - James 1:13-14 - 1 Peter 5:8-9

Day 298 – Angry

James 1:19-20 - Ephesians 4:26 - Proverbs 15:1 - Psalm 37:8

Day 299 – Experiencing fear

2 timothy 1:7 - Romans 8:15 - 1 John 4:18
Isaiah 54:10

Day 300 – Confidence

Philippians 4:13 - Hebrew 13:6 - Habakkuk 3:19
1 John 5:14-15

Day 301 – The body of Christ

1 Corinthians 12:12-13 - Colossians 3:16-17 - 1 Peter 2:9

Day 302 – Discipleship

John 13:35 - John 8:31-32 - John 15:8

Day 303 – Suffering

Psalm 91:1-2 - Psalm 138:7 - John 14:27

Day 304 – Reading the bible

James 1:25 - 1 Peter 2:2 - Hebrews 4:12

Day 305 – The worker in the vineyard

Matthew 20:1-16

Day 306 – Sin

Romans 5:12,19 - 2 Corinthians 5:21 - 1 Peter 3:18

Day 307 – Feeling empty

Romans 15:13 - Psalm 81:10 - 2 Corinthians 12:10

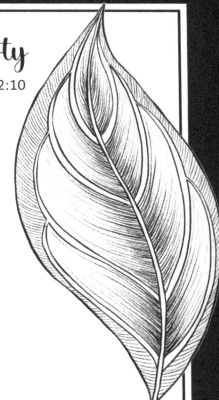

Day 308 – Feeling like giving up

Galatians 6:9 - Deuteronomy 31:6 - Psalm 28:7 - Hebrews 12:1

Day 309 – I need hope

Psalm 119:76 - Psalm 62:5 - Psalm 119:114 - 2 Thessalonians 2:16-17

Day 310 - Overwhelmed

Psalm 142:3 - Isaiah 40:28 - I Samuel 2:2 - Psalm 37:5

Day 311 - Not good enough

Romans 8:1 - Ephesians 1:6 - 1 peter 2:9 - Ephesians 2:4-6

Day 312 – Forgiving yourself

Isaiah 44:22 - Isaiah 43:25 - I John 1:9 - Ephesians 1:7

Day 313 – Blessings

Ezekiel 34:26 - Ephesians 1:3 - Psalm 84:5 - Psalm 128:1

Day 314 – Confusion

Philippians 1:9-10 - Psalm 86:11 - Jeremiah 10:23 - Psalm 32:8

Day 315 – Discipline

Psalm 94:12-14 - Proverbs 3:11-12 - Revelation 3:19
Proverbs 6:23

Day 316 – The weeds

Matthew 13:24-30

Day 317 – Excellence

Matthew 4:19 - John 14:12 - Matthew 20:26-28 - John 15:8

Day 318 – Longing

2 Thessalonians 1:11 - Micah 4:2 - Psalm 84:11

Day 319 – Prayer

Matthew 7:7 - 1 Peter 3:12 - John 14:14 - 1 John 5:14-15

Day 320 – Protection

2 Samuel 23:31 - Psalm 18:30 - Psalm 116:6 - Psalm 12:7 - Psalm 31:23

Day 321 – How can I be wise?

Proverbs Chapter 3

Day 322 – Sickness

Psalm 73:26 - Jeremiah 33:6 - James 5:14-15 - Jeremiah 17:14 - Psalm 119:76

Day 323 – Weakness

1 Chronicles 16:11 - Psalm 73:13 - Ephesians 3;16 - 2 Corinthians 12:9

Day 324 – Path of life

Proverbs 4:26 - Psalm 16:11 - Acts 2:28
Proverbs 15:24 - Proverbs 4:18

Day 325 – Focus

2 Corinthians 4:18 - Matthew 6:33 - Philippians 2:4 - Proverbs 4:27 - Philippians 3:20

Day 326 – Foolish people

Psalms 73:22 - Galatians 3:3-4 - 1 Corinthians 3:18

Day 327 – A lamp on a stand

Mark 4:21-22

Day 328 – Paise the Lord!

Psalm 106:1 - Psalm 112:1 - Romans 15:1 - Psalm 148:2-5

Day 329 – Formulas for success

Proverbs 16:3 - James 1:5 - Joshua 1:8 - Matthew 6:32-33 - Psalms 57:2

Day 330 – Foundations

Ephesians 2:19-22 - Romans 15:20 - 1 Timothy 3:14-15 - Matthew 7:24-27

Day 331 – Accountability

Proverbs 27:17 - Matthew 12:36-37 - Luke 17:3 - Luke 12:47-48

Day 332 – Freedom from fear

Psalm 34:4 - Psalm 46 1:3 - John 14:27 - Romans 8:15

Day 333 – Fight of faith

Matthew 16:18 - Ephesians 3:16 - 1 Timothy 6:12 - 1 John 2:14

Day 334 – Victory

Exodus 14:13-14 - Hebrews 13:6 - 1 John 3:8 - Revelation 12:11

Day 335 – The absent householder

Mark 13:34-37

Day 336 – Results of unrighteous anger

Proverbs 15:18 - Psalms 37:8 - Proverbs 30:33

Day 337 – Keys to overcoming anger

Proverbs 19:11 - Proverbs 14:29 - Matthew 5:21-24

Day 338 – Best short bible verses

1Thessalonians 5:16-18 - 1 John 4:19 - Luke 10:27 - 1 Corinthians 16:14

Day 339 – Christian character

Philippians 4:8 - Romans 12:2 - 2 Peter 1:5-7 - 1 John 4:8

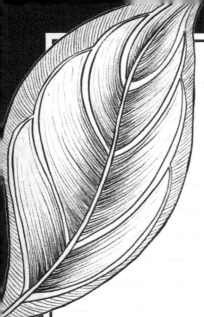

Day 340 – Correction

Hebrews 12:5-11 - Proverbs 12:1 - Proverbs 8:33

Day 341 – Keeping promises

Numbers 30:2 - Ecclesiastes 5:4-5 - Matthew 5:33,37

Day 342 – The fear of God

Proverbs 9:10 - Psalm 111:10 - Proverbs 19:23 - Proverbs 1:7

Day 343 – Glory of God

John 11:40 - Isaiah 42:8 - Romans 3:23 - Exodus 24:17
John 17:4-5 - Revelation 21:11

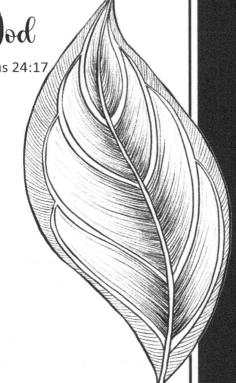

Day 344 – Overcoming negative thinking

1 Peter 5:8 - Proverbs 3:5-6 - Mark 11:23 - Galatians 5:22 - 1 Thessalonians 5:18

Day 345 – Image of God

Genesis 1:27 - Colossians 3:10 - Colossians 1:15 - Philippians 3:21

Day 346 – The two sons

Matthew 21:28-32

Day 347 – War in heaven

Revelation 12:7-12 - Jude 1:9 - 2 Peter 2:4

Day 348 – Aging

2 Corinthians 4:16 - Proverbs 16:31 - Job 12:12
Philippians 3:20-21 - James 4:14

Day 349 – New cloth on old garment

Luke 5:36

Day 350 – Prediction of the future

2 Peter 1:20-21 - Deuteronomy 18:22 - Revelation 22:7 - Jeremiah 29:11

Day 351 – Mediums

Leviticus 19:31 - Isaiah 8:18 - Leviticus 20:27
1 Chronicles 10:13-14

Day 352 – The ten virgins

Matthew 25:1-13

Day 353 – Honoring the parents

Deuteronomy 5:16 - Ephesians 6:1-4 - Exodus 21:17

Day 354 – Helping the helpless

Proverbs 31:8-9 - Isaiah 25:4 - Romans 5:8 - Acts 9:11

Day 355 – House of God

1 Corinthians 3:16 - 1 Timothy 3:14-15 - 1 Peter 2:5

Day 356 – The growing seed

Mark 4:26-29

Day 357 – Body of Christ

Galatians 3:26-29 - Romans 12:4-5 - Colossians 3:15 - Galatians 6:10

Day 358 – Burden

Galatians 6:2 - Matthew 11:28-30 - Hebrews 13:17 - 1 Peter 5:7

Day 359 – The watchful servants

Luke 12:35-40

Day 360 – Christlikeness

1 Thessalonians 1:6 - Ephesians 2:10 - 2 Corinthians 3:18

Day 361 – Discipleship

John 8:31-32 - Acts 14:21-22

Day 362 – Fruitfulness

John 15:5,8 - Luke 3:8 - Matthew 13:22

Day 363 – The creditor and the two debtors

Luke 7:41-43

Day 364 - Eternal life

Galatians 6:7-8 - Romans 6:23 - John 10:28-30

Day 365 - A friend in need

Luke 11:5-13